# BATMAN'S JOURNAL

Testing, testing, 1 ... 2 ... 3 ... BATMAN ...

TESTING OUT MY PEN TO SEE IF
IT WORKS ... IT DOES, OH GOOD.

# I AM BATMAN!

## THE DARK KNIGHT'S ACTIVITY JOURNAL

TEXT (THAT'S THE WORDS) ACTIVITIES, DRAWINGS,
PICTURES AND THE REST ARE ALL DONE
BY
**BATMAN**
(THAT'S ME!)

AREN'T I HANDSOME? ☺

# I AM BATMAN.

AND I'VE DECIDED TO START A JOURNAL FOR MY GREATEST FANS! BECAUSE I DON'T JUST HAVE FANS ...

I HAVE THE GREATEST FANS!

BECAUSE I'M BATMAN

AND YOU, MY FANS, ARE AMAZING.

SO, THIS IS WHAT I WANTED TO WRITE ...

HMM ... THIS 'WRITING A JOURNAL' LARK ISN'T ALL THAT EASY.

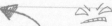

PORTRAIT OF TEMPORARY
CREATIVE BLOCK.

MAYBE IT'S BEST TO START WITH A PICTURE OF ONE
OF MY **GREATEST FANS.**

DRAW A PICTURE OR STICK A PHOTO OF YOURSELF HERE,
WHILE I GATHER MY THOUGHTS ...

OK, IT'S TIME TO HAVE SOME FUN. LET'S START WITH

**THE COOLEST INTRODUCTION TO A BOOK EVER ...**

# ALL THE GREATS

WROTE JOURNALS.

UNFORTUNATELY, THE NOT-SO-GREATS WROTE THEM TOO.

BUT THIS BOOK IS GOING TO BE GREAT BECAUSE WE'RE WORKING ON IT TOGETHER.

SO TURN THE PAGE AND START READING THE GREATEST BOOK OF THE DECADE ... NO, OF THE CENTURY!

# HERE'S HOW TO DRAW MY PORTRAIT IN THREE SIMPLE STEPS:

**STEP 1**

DRAW THE SHAPE OF MY
HEAD AND SHOULDERS.

**STEP 2**

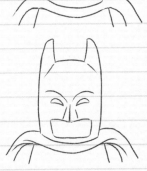

DRAW MY MASK AND EYES.

**STEP 3**

AND THEN DRAW THE REST
OF ME LIKE THIS!
HERE IT IS - PERFECTION.

(ROUND OF

# APPLAUSE

PLEASE!)

# DRAW A PICTURE OF YOURSELF DRESSED AS BATMAN HERE.

YOU'RE READY TO FIGHT CRIME!

THERE'S ONLY ONE REAL BATMAN ... BUT YOU LOOK GREAT!

DRAW A COOL VEHICLE FOR YOURSELF HERE, TOO!

**Has anything exciting happened today?**
Well, I saved the city again.
The night patrol was an absolute pleasure.

First, **JEWELS** were stolen from the museum!

But I did my shadow trick ...
This is the one where I suddenly
emerge from the darkness
waving my cape and my shadow
looks like a giant bat.

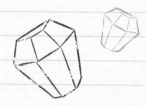

Sometimes I really enjoy
watching villains get

**SCARED!**

Then, there was a bank robbery.
They really should know better than to try
a break-in with me protecting the city.
And in the morning I had to deal with a street
gang of brick thieves ...

# I'M SO FAST THAT
# SOMETIMES
# I AMAZE MYSELF!

BUT I DEALT WITH THEM QUICKLY AND EVEN HAD TIME
TO WONDER WHERE ALL THE SUPER-VILLAINS WERE,
I HADN'T SEEN ANY OF THEM.
NOT EVEN THE JOKER!

COULD IT BE THAT
THEY'RE PLANNING
SOMETHING IN
HIDING?

TIME FOR ME TO TELL YOU AN INTERESTING FACT: EVERY SUPER HERO HAS AN

# ARCH-NEMESIS!

A NEMESIS IS AN OPPONENT WHO CAN SOMETIMES MAKE YOU REALLY ANGRY. ESPECIALLY SOMEONE LIKE THIS BIG NUISANCE, THE JOKER - PICTURED BELOW.

WHAT SUPERPOWERS
DO THEY HAVE?

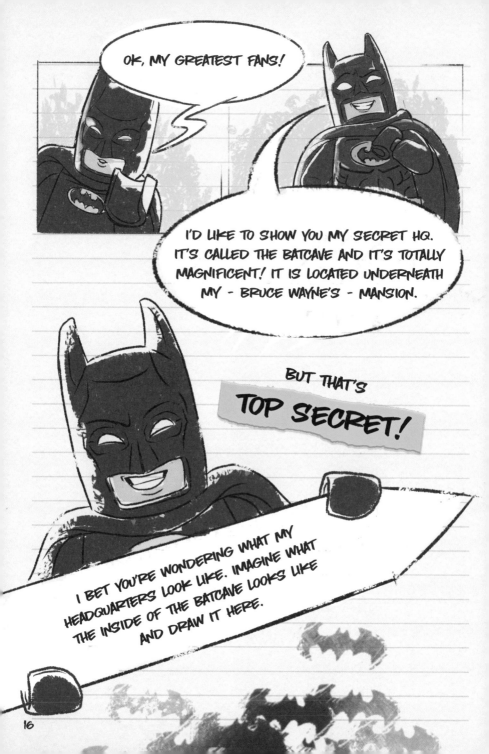

SECRET HQ

# AND NOW SOME FACTS ABOUT ME:

- I KNOW OVER **127** MARTIAL ARTS STYLES (TAKE THAT!)

- THEY CALL ME THE **WORLD'S GREATEST DETECTIVE** (AND THEY'RE PROBABLY RIGHT!)

- MANY SAY I AM UNBELIEVABLY **SMART AND WITTY** (AND I THANK THEM VERY MUCH FOR IT.)

MAN! THIS KICK IS REALLY AWESOME!

- MY COSTUME IS REALLY IMPRESSIVE (WELL, THEY DO SAY 'DRESS TO IMPRESS'!)

- MY VEHICLES ARE SO COOL (IT'S ALWAYS BEST TO TRAVEL IN STYLE!)

- MY FRIEND AND LOYAL BUTLER'S NAME IS ALBERT PENNYWORTH (I LOVE HIM!)

ONE OF THESE FUN FACTS IS **INCORRECT!** BUT WHICH ONE IS IT? LOOK FOR THE ANSWER IN THIS BOOK. ☺

HAS ANYTHING EXCITING HAPPENED TODAY?

## WELL, I SAVED THE CITY AGAIN!

MY OPPONENTS CALL THEMSELVES

# THE ROGUES.

AND I'M SURE I DON'T NEED TO REMIND YOU WHO GATHERED THEM ALL TOGETHER!

THEY TRIED TO TAKE CONTROL OF GOTHAM'S ENERGY FACILITY

## AND THAT WAS A BIG MISTAKE!

DON'T WORRY, I SOON MADE THEM REALISE THEIR

# MISTAKE!

HEE HEE HEE!

BAM!

PAF!

WHAM! AND THOSE RASCALS FOUND THEMSELVES FACE DOWN IN THE STREET ...

# DESIGN SOME NEW GADGETS FOR ME.

## REMEMBER TO USE

### THE BAT-SYMBOL IN YOUR DRAWINGS ...

I'D LOVE A JET BACKPACK TOO, WHILE YOU'RE AT IT!

ALFRED TAKES CARE OF ALL MY GADGETS AND KEEPS EVERYTHING IN ORDER.

# I'M NOT SURE

IF I'VE FORMALLY INTRODUCED

## ALFRED

TO YOU.

HE'S MY **FRIEND** AND BUTLER, AND HE USED TO BE AN **ACTOR!**

TO BE OR NOT TO BE ...

DRAW **ALFRED** STARRING IN AN AMAZING MOVIE RIGHT HERE ON THIS PAGE!

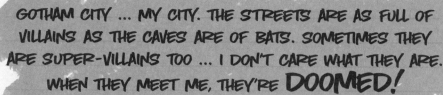

GOTHAM CITY ... MY CITY. THE STREETS ARE AS FULL OF VILLAINS AS THE CAVES ARE OF BATS. SOMETIMES THEY ARE SUPER-VILLAINS TOO ... I DON'T CARE WHAT THEY ARE. WHEN THEY MEET ME, THEY'RE **DOOMED!**

HERE IS A VILLAIN

TRY BEING ME FOR A MOMENT AND MATCH THESE VILLAINS TO THEIR SHADOWS IN THE PICTURE ABOVE.

# AS A SUPER HERO

I HAVE SOME PRETTY **AWESOME LINES** TO SAY TO SUPER-VILLAINS.

IN MY SPARE TIME I LIKE TO JOT DOWN COOL LINES TO USE IN THE FUTURE. HERE ARE SOME EXAMPLES:

## THAT'S REALLY IMPRESSIVE

CAN YOU SEE MY FACE? IT'S THE FACE OF JUSTICE!

(WARNING! NEVER USE THIS LINE IN A DARK ALLEY.)

YOU THINK YOU KNOW NO FEAR? I'M YOUR BIGGEST FEAR!

(WARNING! ONLY USE THIS LINE IN DARK ALLEYS.)

# IT'S TIME FOR US TO MAKE THE PARTY A LITTLE MORE EXCITING.

## FINISH THE COMIC STRIP, BUT MAKE THE ENDING ON THE NEXT FEW PAGES REALLY AWESOME!

# HAS ANYTHING EXCITING HAPPENED TODAY?

## WELL, I SAVED THE CITY AGAIN!

THE **JOKER** ATTACKED THE CITY. HE BREEZED INTO COMMISSIONER GORDON'S RETIREMENT BALL. HE APPEARED OUT OF THE BLUE.

## AND, AS USUAL, HE PUT ON AN ACT!

## BRUCE WAYNE NEEDED TO BECOME BATMAN!

## AND JUST WHEN I WAS ABOUT TO TRY MY NEW ...

# THE JOKER HAS CROSSED PATHS WITH ME TOO MANY TIMES ...

DRAW THE JOKER GETTING ON MY NERVES **HERE!**

BUT IT'S ALWAYS **FUN** IN THE END!

!!!

I JUST NEED TO THINK ABOUT HOW TO STOP HIM ONCE AND FOR ALL!

# I'M A TALENTED ARTIST!

I HAVE BEEN DOODLING A BIT. THERE'S NOTHING QUITE LIKE DOODLING. IT HELPS ME RELAX AND IT'S MY FAVOURITE THING TO DO. OK, SO MAYBE I'M EXAGGERATING A LITTLE. I DO ALSO LIKE SAVING THE CITY FROM TIME TO TIME TOO. AND THEN I DOODLE ON THEIR WANTED POSTERS!

# WANTED

# WANTED

# WANTED

# WANTED

NOW IT'S YOUR TURN TO DOODLE ON THE POSTERS OF THE UNLUCKY GUYS WHO DARED TO CROSS PATHS WITH ME!

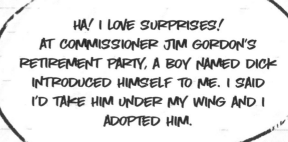

HA! I LOVE SURPRISES! AT COMMISSIONER JIM GORDON'S RETIREMENT PARTY, A BOY NAMED DICK INTRODUCED HIMSELF TO ME. I SAID I'D TAKE HIM UNDER MY WING AND I ADOPTED HIM.

HERE ARE A COUPLE OF PHOTOS OF **US** TOGETHER.

# CAN YOU DRAW US POSING IN SOME MORE PICS?

## I DO **LOVE** A SELFIE OR TWO, OR THREE OR MORE!

DICK STILL THINKS THAT BATMAN AND BRUCE WAYNE ARE
TWO DIFFERENT PEOPLE! OH WELL!

# HOW TO BE A SUPER HERO

## PART 1 (THEORY)

THIS IS GOING TO BE HARDER THAN I FIRST THOUGHT! NOW, WHERE DO I START?

WILL MR. WAYNE BE JOINING US AS WELL?

# WHAT ARE THE FIRST THINGS YOU NEED TO DO AS A YOUNG SUPER HERO?

- FIRST, DECIDE WHETHER YOU WANT TO USE YOUR POWERS FOR GOOD OR EVIL.

- AND SECOND ... YOU'D BETTER NOT CHOOSE EVIL, I'M TELLING YOU ... DON'T!

- THEN YOU MUST CHOOSE AN AWESOME OUTFIT. (TRY LOOKING FOR INSPIRATION FROM THE ANIMAL WORLD.)

- NEXT, MAKE SURE YOU HAVE SOME CRIME-FIGHTING TRICKS UP YOUR SLEEVE!

- FILL IN SOME MORE THINGS HERE:

SOMETIMES I THINK ABOUT
HOW MYSTERIOUS I AM.

I'M BATMAN,
A SUPER HERO
WITH A HEART FULL OF SECRETS
AND DARKNESS.

SURELY THERE COULDN'T BE ANYTHING
MORE MYSTERIOUS OUT THERE ...

EXCEPT FOR THE MYSTERY OF WHY NOBODY RECOGNISES
THAT CLARK KENT IS SUPERMAN!

THEY ARE ONLY GLASSES!
WHY CAN'T ANYONE SEE THAT?

SO WHERE WAS I? OH, THAT'S IT
... SECRETS. HERE ARE
SOME OF MINE ...

## SECRET 1
(A SMALL ONE)

ONE POCKET IN MY UTILITY BELT IS FOR SPARE SOCKS!

## SECRET 2

I'D LIKE TO CARVE THE BAT-SYMBOL ONTO THE SIDE OF THE MOON AND THEN SEE THE LOOK ON THE JOKER'S FACE!

## SECRET 3
(THE BIGGEST ONE)

WHEN I STAY IN THE BATCAVE TOO LONG, I LOSE TRACK OF WHETHER IT'S DAY OR NIGHT, AND I START FEELING A BIT LONELY ...

BUT DON'T WORRY, I SOON GET OVER IT BY HANGING WITH MY BAT FRIENDS!

WRITE SOME OF YOUR TOP SECRETS HERE.
FEEL FREE TO WRITE IN SECRET CODE SHOULD YOU NEED TO.

# I HAVE JUST NOTICED IN MY CALENDAR THAT

THE ANNUAL JUSTICE LEAGUE PARTY IS BEING HELD TODAY!

I WASN'T INVITED AGAIN!

(AND I WASN'T INVITED TO THE 56 PREVIOUS PARTIES EITHER. MAYBE I SHOULD WORK ON MY TEAMWORK SKILLS?)

I PREDICT THAT **BARBARA GORDON**, GOTHAM CITY'S NEW POLICE COMMISSIONER,

IS GOING TO BE **BATGIRL**

AND MY INTUITION IS NEVER WRONG.

BARBARA WILL TRANSFORM INTO ...
**BATGIRL!**

LOOK AT BARBARA'S OUTFITS.
CAN YOU DESIGN ONE FOR HER TOO?

# HOW TO BE A SUPER HERO

## PART 2

(PRACTISE!)

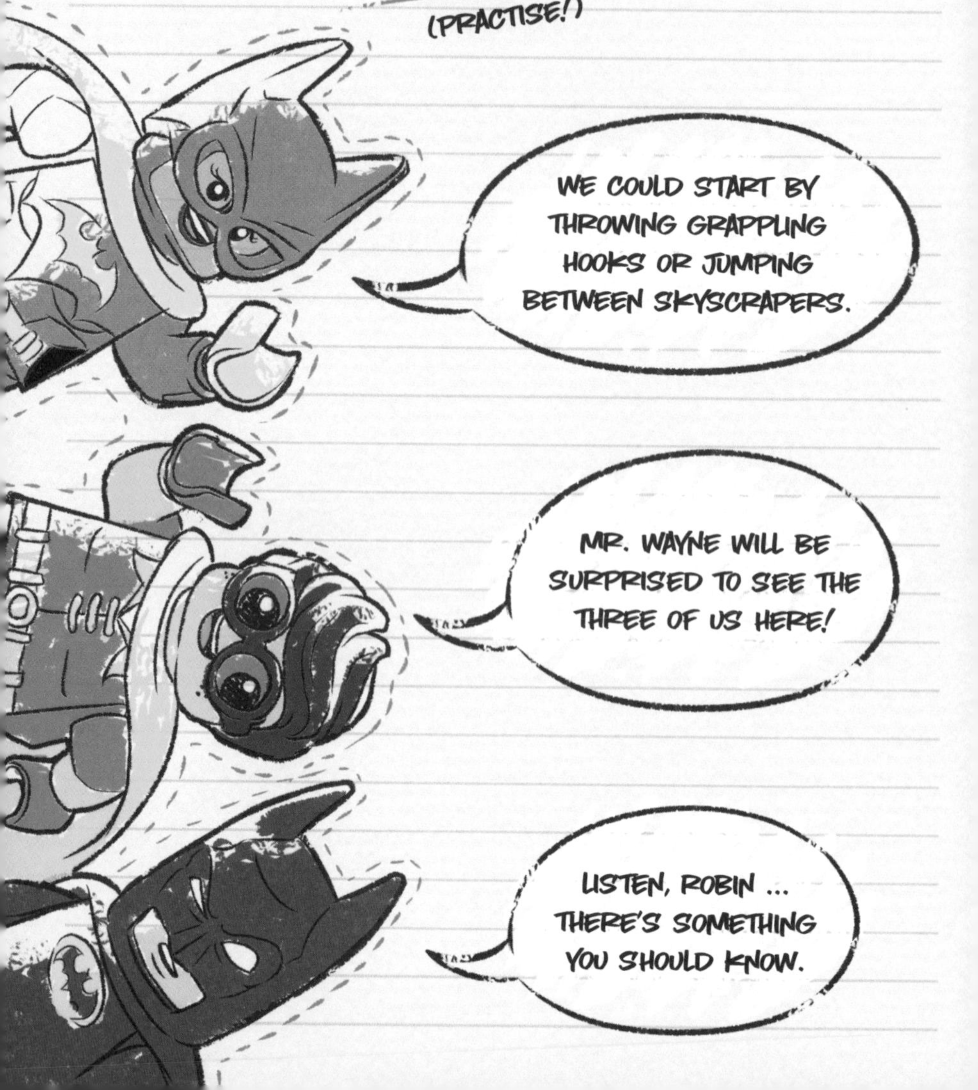

# DRAW SOME PICTURES OF ME TRAINING ROBIN HERE.

I CAN'T STOP THINKING ABOUT THAT

CLOWN

THE JOKER!

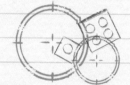

I NEED TO GET RID OF HIM

# ONCE AND FOR ALL.

I JUST DON'T KNOW WHAT THE BEST
WAY TO DO THAT IS YET ... _^_"

COULD I SEND HIM UP TO
THE MOON ON A ROCKET?

OR PACK HIM UP AND POST
HIM TO A DESERTED ISLAND
SOMEWHERE ...

OR MAYBE I COULD
ARRANGE FOR HIM TO BE
ABDUCTED BY
ALIENS?

# CAN YOU THINK OF SOME OTHER INVENTIVE WAYS TO GET RID OF THE JOKER?

# BRUCE WAYNE, AGED 9

## ✓ A SUPER HERO:

✓ SAVES THE WORLD. FIGHTS MIGHTY
SUPER-VILLAINS WITH COSMIC POWERS.
(AMBITIOUS BUT NOT IMPOSSIBLE.)

✓ WEARS THE COOLEST COSTUME, PREFERABLY
WITH A MASK, ARMOUR AND THE MOST AWESOME
SYMBOL EVER!

✓ HAS TONS OF GADGETS ... FIRING ROPES, HOOKS,
SHURIKENS, EXPLODING ORBS, SMOKE GRENADES,
NIGHT VISION DEVICES, WINGED CAPES THAT TURN
INTO PARAGLIDERS!

✓ DEFEATS VILLAINS USING KUNG FU, KARATE, JUDO,
NINJUTSU, JIU-JITSU, BRAZILIAN JIU-JITSU, AIKIDO,
BOXING, THAI BOXING, TAE KWON DO, CAPOEIRA, KENDO,
KYUDO. (I DON'T KNOW ANY MORE MARTIAL ARTS BUT IT
WOULD BE GOOD TO LEARN MORE THAN 127.)

✓ OWNS HUGE BATTLE MACHINES THAT FLY, FLOAT,
RIDE, CRUSH AND SHOOT ... ALL WITH AMAZING
STYLE AND TOTAL WOW FACTOR!

WHO SHOULD I BECOME IN THE FUTURE?
A **SUPER HERO** OR A **BILLIONAIRE** BUSINESSMAN?

## A BILLIONAIRE BUSINESSMAN:

 EARNS MONEY AND LIVES COMFORTABLY.
(NOT SURE HOW TO LIVE COMFORTABLY IF
I NEED TO EARN MONEY ALL THE TIME?)

 WEARS A SUIT, A PAIR OF TRAINERS AND ALL
THE LATEST TRENDS TO THE MANAGEMENT
BOARD MEETINGS.

HAS AN ELEGANT NOTEBOOK AND COMPUTER
(WITH AT LEAST 100 GAMES, IN CASE I'M 'BORED'
AT THE 'BOARD' MEETING ... GET IT?)

 GOES TO WEEKLY MANAGEMENT BOARD MEETINGS.
(I NEED TO FIND OUT WHAT THIS 'BOARD' ACTUALLY
IS, BUT I'M PRETTY SURE IT'S NOT RELATED TO A
SKATEBOARD, WHICH IS A SHAME.)

 OWNS A FANCY LIMO, YACHT, MAYBE
A JET SKATEBOARD FOR THE YACHT
(OR FOR THE BOARD MEETINGS).

## HEY, WHY NOT BOTH! ☺

# WHO WILL YOU BECOME IN THE FUTURE?

## A SUPER HERO
### OR SOMETHING ELSE ENTIRELY?

DRAW AND DESCRIBE YOUR FUTURE SELF HERE.

I AM BATMAN AND I AM ... OUT OF SPACE IN MY
JOURNAL ... MAYBE IT'S A SIGN FOR ME TO LEAP
INTO ACTION! ALL RIGHT, MY AWESOME FANS,
BATMAN IS PUTTING DOWN HIS PEN.
LOOK OUT FOR ME IN GOTHAM CITY!